CW00696357

CONTE....

Inspired by the MHF's Brain by Ian Banks • Text by Fabio Zucchelli, Richard Shrubb and Steve Baxter • Edited by Jim Pollard • Cartoons by John Byrne Images: MHF and creativecommons.org. Credits p33.
Publication: August 2014
Last revision: April 2017 • Next revision: April 2020

IN THE UK, 12 MEN TAKE THEIR OWN LIVES <u>EVERY SINGLE DAY</u>.

DON'T WORRY, BE HAPPY

Don't worry, be happy. It's easier said than done. But if you can crack it, even a little, you'll get a lot more out of life. This booklet is full of good ideas to give your mind an MOT. Acting on just one could make the difference.

Inspired by the ground-breaking Brain manual by Dr Ian Banks, Beat Stress, Feel Better has been written by three professional health writers with personal experience of some of the challenges discussed in this booklet.

It has been fully referenced and researched under the Department of Health Information Standard and reviewed and approved by the MHF's medical peer review panel chaired by Dr John Chisholm.

TOO MUCH STRESS CAN:

> DAMAGE YOUR IMMUNE SYSTEM AND HEART

> INCREASE YOUR CHANCE OF SERIOUS HEALTH PROBLEMS

> REDUCE YOUR LIFE-EXPECTANCY

> DAMAGE YOUR SEX LIFE

WHY STRESS IS STRESSFUL

Stress is normal. It is what we feel when a situation is hard to handle.

Adrenaline rushes through the body, increasing heart rate and boosting mental and physical alertness. We feel sweaty, tingly and get butterflies. This 'fight or flight' response was very useful to our ancestors coping with physical threats such as a marauding mammoth or sabre-toothed tiger.

Today's 'threats' are often far less serious but far more frequent. The trouble is that stress hormones such as adrenaline and cortisol are harmful when we don't actually need them. Over time, they can damage the immune system and the heart and reduce both physical and mental well-being.

This means it's not healthy - or practical - to go into 'fight or flight' mode every five minutes. It's much easier - and healthier - to respond in a less stressful way. But how do you do that? If we can figure out how we feel and what has caused it, we can respond more smartly. That's what this booklet is all about. The first part - starting on page 6 - looks at common causes of stress, the second part - starting on page 17 - looks at what we can do about it.

WHAT CAUSES STRESS?

Life can be a right pain in the arse at times. Here are some of the common causes of stress today. Which of them push your buttons?

WORK

Stress, depression and anxiety are the main causes of days off work in the UK. British men work longer hours than European men - less time for us and our families. Insecure jobs and contracts increase stress.

But do our attitudes to work make it worse? The pressure to 'succeed' from school onwards promotes competition and comparison. You might say this motivates us. But does it? After all, no matter how well we're doing, there'll always be someone doing better. How will we ever be content? Work to live. Don't live to work.

> Speak to someone at work responsible for occupational health.

> Leave work at work – don't answer work emails or work calls at home.

> Talk to a trade union – visit tuc.org.uk.

> Perhaps ask your employer for flexible working.

> If you have a family, visit workingfamilies.org.uk.

WHY UNDERSTANDING STRESS MATTERS

Stress causes mental health problems.

One in four of us will have a mental health problem this year. They're responsible for half of all long-term absences from work.

Unchecked mental health problems can be very serious indeed.

About three-quarters of the people treated for depression are women but about three quarters of the people who commit suicide are men. Since depression is a major cause of suicide, something doesn't add up. Is it us?

Talking about stress is not a sign of weakness. It takes balls.

UNEMPLOYMENT

Unemployment is often not your fault, however it might feel. Try to make use of government services such as Jobcentre Plus and Universal Jobmatch on gov.uk and make sure you claim all the benefits you're entitled to. Billions of pounds go unclaimed every year in Jobseeker's Allowance and other benefits.

MONEY

Whether it's struggling with bills, long-term debt or over-spending on Christmas presents, money means stress. Try not to get into debt in the first place but you're not alone if you do. It's never too late to seek money advice but sooner is always better.

> Talk to the Citizens Advice Bureau (CAB) (citizensadvice.org.uk) or the government's free Money Advice Service (moneyadviceservice.org.uk)

> Go to a local credit union rather than a payday lender. This can save a lot of money as interest rates can be 12% instead of 2000%. Visit findyourcreditunion.co.uk

> The NHS has an online tool to help you see the effect money worries are having on your mental health. See page 32.

ENDINGS

Don't underestimate the impact of grief on your well-being. The death of a loved one brings several stages of grief. Give yourself time to grieve. If you need support, try Cruse (see page 33) or other grief counsellors.

But it's not just death. Other life changes which shock and to which we need to adjust include moving house, splitting up with a partner, changing job or children leaving the family home.

HEALTH AND MOOD

Physical health changes affect your head too. Feeling unwell or being in pain makes it harder to cope with other challenges; adjusting to a longer-term condition involves grieving for the old you.

Many long-term conditions can directly affect mood including thyroid disorder, diabetes, Parkinson's Syndrome or multiple sclerosis. So can the diagnosis of a serious illness.

In all cases, your GP should offer advice on counselling, medication and other support for your well-being as well as on the physical disease itself.

Undiagnosed conditions such as dyslexia or ADHD (see page 29) can also cause stress and anxiety and lead to relationship difficulties and bullying.

I THINK I'VE GOT "SEASONAL AFFECTIVE DISORDER" - EVERY TIME THE FOOTBALL SEASON FINISHES I FEEL TERRIBLE...

WEATHER AND THE WINTER BLUES

We all need daylight and the sun on our skins. Grey skies are gloomy. Being too hot or too cold will also affect your mood.

Seasonal Affective Disorder (SAD) - or 'winter depression' - is linked to low exposure to sunlight.

If you find yourself regularly despairing during darker days,

talk to your GP. There is stuff available including special lightboxes.

Visit sada.org.uk.

NO MAN IS AN ISLAND

PARTNERS AND FRIENDS

Love hurts. Relationships, family disputes and struggles with your identity and sexuality can be a huge factor in happiness. Social media 'friends' provide a distraction but may jeopardise other real relationships.

The only advice that works is: find a time to talk. It may be uncomfortable but bottling it up is worse. There's no right way to talk about this stuff – just say it how you feel it. (If you're worried you'll lose your temper, see page 15 for tips.)

The talking therapies (see page 23) discussed in this booklet are particularly useful for relationship problems. Relate (relate.org.uk) and other organisations provide talking therapies for individuals, couples and families.

SEXUALITY

Be who you are. If your sexuality isn't harming anyone else, enjoy it. (If it is,

get help before you commit a crime.) If you need to talk to someone about your sexuality and you don't know a local organisation, there are some suggestions under Who Can Help? on page 32.

DRINK AND DRUGS

What goes up must come down. This is generally the case with alcohol and all other drugs including prescription ones if taken in too large a quantity. Even smoking can drag your mood down in the long term.

As well as your physical health, the hangover will often affect the way you feel about yourself. You may feel anxious, depressed and disgusted with yourself. Long term, drinking too much too often can cause serious mental health problems including severe depression, paranoia and hallucinations which can only be sorted by a doctor.

An active social life is good for you but it all adds up. If you're concerned about overdoing it, see 'Am I addicted?' on page 16.

ARE YOU LIVING A LIE?

We're all different, we're all unique. Living a lie is pretending to be someone you're not - even to yourself.

We might hide it behind all sorts of things including drink, aggression and even hard work, but a lot of us are not comfortable in our skin. Perhaps it is related to childhood, family, culture, sexuality, ideas of right and wrong (see Get To Know Your Triggers on page 14). We're not responsible for what happened to us as kids but only we can do something about it as adults.

Be honest with yourself, especially if you're often angry or feel disrespected. Then, if you can, find someone else you can be honest with. It doesn't have to be a mate or family member. Try one of the organisations listed in this booklet. Feeling uncomfortable in your own skin won't get better with time. Most likely it will get worse.

Old-fashioned ideas of what it means to be a man can make it difficult for us to talk honestly. Some of us can't even ask for directions in the street because we don't want to look vulnerable. But silence isn't a sign of strength. Silence is easy: you just keep your mouth shut. Being honest is the real strength. Accept yourself as you are and be fine with it.

If you're not hurting yourself or anyone else, what's wrong with being yourself? (Even if that is different from what you think society and other people want.)

WARNING SIGNS

A relentless build-up of pressure, without the opportunity to recover, can lead to harmful stress. The important thing is to recognise the warning signs while you can do something about it.

Common signs are:

> Eating more or less than normal

> Mood swings

> Low self-esteem

> Feeling tense or anxious

> Not sleeping properly (or wanting to sleep all the time)

> Poor memory or forgetfulness

> Excessive drinking and/or drug use.

> Feeling really tired and lacking in energy

> Withdrawing from family and friends

> Behaving out of character

> Finding it hard to concentrate and struggling at work

> Losing interest in things you usually enjoy

> Having unusual experiences, like seeing or hearing things that others don't.

> There may be physical signs too like headaches, irritable bowel syndrome or aches and pains.

URBAN BLUES

Most of us live in towns. We interact, travel and communicate more than in rural areas. Add in unhealthy workplaces, noise and fast food and it's not a recipe for calm.

Make your space less stressful by, for example:

> Removing clutter

> Making it more personal – putting up a family photo at work

> Making a sanctuary – removing intrusions (especially electronic ones) in one room (especially the bedroom).

LONELINESS

More of us are living alone, further from our families, relationship break-ups are high and communities are less tight. In the UK, one in ten people feel lonely and half think we're getting lonelier. We're social animals; loneliness makes us unhappy. If you're down, it could be you're lonely.

THIS IS A REALLY POWERFUL ARTICLE ON LONELINESS— SHAME I HAVE NOBODY TO DISCUSS IT WITH...

WHAT WORKS?

So how do you change your response to stress? There are no rules. Different things work for different people. These ideas will help both reduce stress and increase your capacity to handle it.

EAT

Nutrition isn't just about physical health. Your brain needs nutrients like the rest of your body. If you eat rubbish you will feel rubbish. This is particularly important if you work unusual hours or shifts

Low levels of vitamins and minerals or changes in blood sugar levels from an irregular or unbalanced diet can affect mood.

If your mood swings for no obvious reason, keep a food diary and see if certain foods, especially ones you eat a lot of, play a role.

An old adage is 'breakfast like a king, lunch like a prince, and dine like a pauper'. With a good breakfast you will be in a good mood as your day begins. Top up through the day after that.

EXERCISE

Taking exercise is proven to blow off the blues. In the short term, two happiness chemicals are released into your system – anandamide and endorphins, the so-called 'runner's high'.

In the long term, exercise improves your all-round fitness. Of course, fit people still get the blues, but the less exercise you take the worse you feel.

For the full 'runner's high', jog, get on your bike or go to the gym. But low intensity exercise works too. Just a good walk will give you a lift. Or anything you fancy that gets the heart beating a little faster.

Do it regularly. Set some simple goals. It'll put some rhythm back into your life. It's fun and you'll feel and sleep better. There's no pill that can do all that.

IF EXERCISE WERE A PILL, EVERYONE WOULD BE TAKING IT.

EATING DISORDERS

Eating disorders such as overeating, anorexia (self-starving) or bulimia (binge-eating and purging/vomiting) affect far more men than we realise. This may be because of an increase in Body Dysmorphic Disorder, where people see themselves as failing to have what they think is the 'ideal body'.

Advice is available from Men Get Eating Disorders Too (mengetedstoo.co.uk), Beat (b-eat.co.uk) and Mind (mind.org.uk). NHS weight management services can offer a personal consultant and exercise and diet plans. Talking therapies are also useful.

LIVE THE MOMENT YOU ARE IN

Ever get out of the car and not remember the journey? This 'autopilot' can drag mood down, especially when we have a lot on our minds. Get off autopilot by noticing what's going on in the moment you're living in. Look up. Listen. Observe. It's tougher than it sounds but worth trying. It's calming and gets things in perspective.

If you feel like you're always in a headlong rush, Mindfulness (or Mindfulness-based Cognitive Therapy or Mindfulness-based stress reduction) can teach you to recognise when your autopilot is dragging you into unhelpful thoughts and to return your attention to the moment, often using the breath as an 'anchor'. Sounds weird? Possibly - but there's a growing body of evidence that it

works. Anyone can do it - there are books and local groups. Ask your GP about it.

SING, DANCE, LAUGH...

Yes really. Singing is good for the heart and the immune system. Just the way you breathe when you sing reduces stress. Singing as part of a group is even better. Join a choir or a football crowd. Sing in the shower.

Dancing – in a nightclub, a ballroom or even your bedroom - boosts your mood too. As well being great exercise.

Laughter, perhaps not surprisingly, also releases happy hormones.

All three are free mood-boosters you can access any time.

CONNECT AND TALK

If loneliness makes us unhappy, then connecting with others will make us happy. We all know how good it is to talk when you really connect with someone. For some of us, social media can only go so far. Indeed, research suggests social media can make some of us miserable.

'A problem shared is a problem halved' is a cliché because it's true. It's not about other people telling us what to do or being needy. It is simply that talking often lets us see the solution for ourselves in a way thinking alone can't. We're not alone - we often share the same problems.

Having a chat about something doesn't have to be a big deal. Share an activity with the person you want to chat to and talk while you're doing it: washing-up, cleaning the car, painting a fence, playing a computer game.

Even if it barely involves talking, connecting with others and feeling part of something in whatever setting feels good: playing five-a-side, going to the pub or underwater basket-weaving. Meet new people through a local club, group or internet meet-up - especially if social media are dominating your life.

DO WHAT YOU ENJOY

It's tempting to drop the things you enjoy the most when you get overloaded. But not doing the good stuff won't make the bad stuff go away. When you feel low, that's when it's most important to do the things you really love. It's often just what you need to feel relaxed and good about yourself.

VOLUNTEER

Volunteering benefits everyone. You can help others, learn new skills, meet like-minded people and do something you enjoy. You may just want to get out of the house.

Whatever it is, volunteering gets you out of yourself and thinking about something - and someone - else. It is especially useful if you're between jobs.

LEARN

Taking a class is great for getting out of a rut. Learning proves - if you need reminding - that things can change for the better.

They say knowledge is its own reward but there is also evidence that it can boost confidence, self-esteem and motivation.

SEX

Sex is a great stress-buster for some. Helps you sleep too. Contact and intimacy is relaxing even if you don't fancy the full works.

GET SOME SLEEP

After a stressful situation, sleep resets the balance. We underperform if we don't sleep. Regular poor sleep also shortens life-expectancy.

The mind needs sleep too. To dream. When people with anxiety or depression are surveyed, most of them sleep for less than six hours a night. (Recurring nighmares can be a sign of post-traumatic stress.) Keep fresh to function. If you're having trouble sleeping, try these:

> a warm bath (not too hot) so your body is at a temperature to rest

> removing TV/computer from the bedroom

> cutting down on booze and caffeine

> relaxation exercises or yoga and/or a relaxation CD (serious exercise will have the opposite effect and keep you awake)

> writing tomorrow's To-Do list to clear your head

> reading or listening to the radio - this can relax the mind by distracting it

> keeping a sleep diary to spot the possible causes of bad sleep for you. Record what you did in the day (especially the hour or two before sleeping) and how well you slept afterwards.

WRITE

Anything creative boosts mood. Hammering away at your guitar, throwing paint at a canvas or dancing around in any way you fancy, it's all good. But unlike say music or art, writing doesn't require any special talent. Anyone can do it. More than that, it's private. There's evidence suggesting that writing about the challenges we're facing and how we feel about them will make us feel better. (Like talking it lets you see things in a different way from thinking alone.) But you can write about whatever you want - fact, fiction.

Not sure how to start? Everyday write down one thing you're grateful for and why.

TALKING TREATMENTS

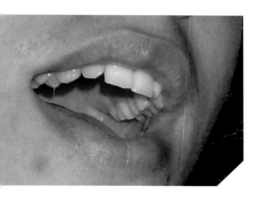

There are many talking therapies. From one-off counselling sessions to long-term, in-depth psychotherapy, each uses a slightly different approach.

Some are one-to-one with a therapist, others are done in groups.

Some men prefer the privacy of individual therapy; others find hearing from others with similar experiences useful. Your call.

CBT

Recently the NHS has become interested in Cognitive Behavioural Therapy (CBT). It works by enabling you to recognise the patterns of thoughts, feelings and behaviour that lead to difficulties in your life, and looking at ways of shifting these patterns through the way you think and what you do.

It doesn't focus on the past but on improving the present.

Unlike some therapy, it may only take a few sessions to help you understand your stress or a bit longer (12 sessions) to help with depression.

The website Living Life to the Full (llttf.com) offers a free introduction to CBT online.

MINDFULNESS

Mindfulness-based Cognitive Therapy (see page 19) combines meditation techniques with CBT. Great if you want a more practical approach and again results can be pretty fast.

If you think that talking therapy might be useful for you, do some research into the various types and talk to your GP. You may even be able to refer yourself under the NHS IAPT initiative (www.iapt.nhs.uk/services).

MEDICATION

In 2012, the number of prescriptions in England for anti-depressants topped 50 million for the first time. But drugs (usually anti-depressants called SSRIs) are no longer the automatic choice for GPs when people go to them with mood or stress problems. Some people find them useful but it's worth doing a bit of research first:

> What are the side-effects?

> How long before they should start working? (Most take 6-8 weeks.)

> How long are you likely to have to take them for?

> Are there alternatives to medication that might work better for you?

> How easy are they to come off?

Their benefits in cases of severe depression are generally accepted but there is debate about how useful they are for mild to moderate cases. Depending on your symptoms, you may need medication to stabilise mood before talking therapies and some of the other ideas discussed in this booklet will begin to help. Discuss it with your GP. Your local pharmacist may also be useful.

KEEP IT SIMPLE

Take control by keeping a routine:

> Get up and go to bed at regular times.

> Set small, manageable goals - like tidying up the house for 15 minutes.

> Focus on taking things 'day by day'- reminding yourself of this when you notice your mind wandering into the past or future.

WORKS FOR ME

WE'RE ALL DIFFERENT BUT...

The three main writers and the cartoonist on Beat Stress, Feel Better all have personal experience of many of the issues discussed in this booklet.

We're all different - but here's what works for them.

I'M GETTING WORRIED ABOUT MY MOOD SWINGS— EVERY TIME I GET IN A MOOD I TAKE A SWING AT SOMEBODY.

FABIO: LEARN TO LOVE YOURSELF

" On the face of it, growing up I really didn't have it hard at all. People often seem surprised to hear I've really struggled with low mood and anxiety. The causes of my decade and a half of depression were quite subtle, mainly to do with beliefs I built up about myself growing up.

The underlying force periodically taking me out of action for months, years even at a time, was self-criticism. And as Yoda would say, self-criticism leads to anger, anger to self-hatred and self-hatred is the path to the dark side.

TO BE HONEST I ORIGINALLY SIGNED UP TO GET MYSELF OUT OF A RUT...

POT HOLING NIGHT CLASS

I've tried drugs and had more types of therapy than Woody Allen. Some helped at the time, some didn't. It was only when I came across mindfulness and compassion-focused therapy that things really started to click. Bulbs have continued to light up ever since.

Practising mindfulness has massively helped, by teaching me to step back from the intensity of difficult thoughts and feelings, to stop myself from overthinking. The compassion part of it, which has been just as important, has been about coming to see myself as like anyone else: great just the way we are. "

ANXIETY

Anxiety is constant worry - sometimes almost an inability to live without worrying about something. As well as a feeling of dread, some anxious people experience physical symptoms such as heart palpitations or dizziness. Types of anxiety include social anxiety (dread of meeting new people), obsessive compulsive disorder (an urge to clean or repeat routines in a certain way) and phobias (irrational fears). Hypnotherapy can treat phobias.

RICHARD: RECOVERY IS A JOURNEY

" I had a massive breakdown in 1996, but didn't get to see a psychiatrist until 1999. To my family my breakdown appeared so gradual they didn't realise I had finally lost the plot. To them I was just a weird alcoholic angry waste of space.

Although I began experiencing symptoms of paranoid schizophrenia from 1996, I had been going downhill for a good five years before.

Getting to grips with my diagnosis was the hard part. Admitting to yourself that you need help is the tough first step to recovery – if you don't, suicide is a real risk.

Take all the support you can and listen to care staff. Listen to fellow patients too. Recovery is a journey and there will be ups and downs, but hold on to the idea that you can beat it and you will.

Recovery took me five years before I did an MA in broadcast journalism and went freelance. I will never stop fighting, but will always take a positive attitude to it. I am disabled, but am a fighter. "

SCHIZOPHRENIA

The exact cause of Schizophrenia is brought on by a combination of genetic and environmental factors and affects the way you think.

It is often widely misunderstood and isn't about "split personalities".

Symptoms include experiencing things that are not real such as hallucinations and paranoia. You may feel things crawling over your body or hear voices. These are sometimes called positive symptoms.

There are also negative symptoms: losing interest in your life and world.

STEVE: I DON'T HAVE TO PRETEND ANYMORE

" I was diagnosed with depression ten years ago – but I had been struggling with it since childhood.

I felt there was something inadequate about me – that everyone else was able to cope and it was just me who wasn't able to live his life in the right way. The shame this brought meant I found it hard to talk about how I was feeling to those closest to me, let alone act.

INTERNATIONAL MIME CONVENTION

MARCEL'S UNDER STRESS AGAIN – BUT HE DOESN'T WANT TO TALK ABOUT IT...

Eventually I saw a GP who understood I was going through depression. Prescribed antidepressants, I began to feel more able to cope with the everyday strains, and learn the difference between 'feeling low' and the more serious chronic depression in my life.

I've found huge support from writing about depression – from other people who are depressed and because I don't have to pretend anymore.

Sometimes if you admit you're vulnerable it can be the strongest thing you can do. "

DEPRESSION

We all feel down from time to time. But with time we get over it.

Depression is feeling sad for weeks, months or longer. It is a normal reaction to too many stressful situations at once. It will affect most people at some time in their lives - about one in ten of us in any one year.

JOHN: I DIDN'T KNOW UNTIL I WAS IN MY FORTIES

"I grew up when things like ADHD and dyslexia hadn't been 'invented' so didn't find out until I was in my early forties.

My 6 year-old son was tested. Teachers thought he had signs of ADHD but when the child psychologist described the symptoms I realised it was me she was describing and any traits my son had were just behaviours of mine he was copying.

I was shocked but when I did some reading it rang lots of bells. There were crazy things I had done and bad decisions which, although they can't be blamed entirely on ADHD, weren't helped by the ADHD tendency to act without any planning and take on too much.

ADHD adults, while often creative and quirky, tend to be extremely forgetful and disorganised. All of us are like this sometimes. The key word is 'extreme'. You can be easily distracted or at another time so focused on one thing that you forget eating, sleeping and other people (relationships often break up over this). Sometimes we self-medicate with drugs, alcohol or high-risk behaviour.

Because I work in drawing and the arts, some of my ADHD behaviour - 'sideways' thinking, creativity, moving from one topic to another - fitted in well. But the chaos in my finances, relationships and other areas that needed focus and clear thinking were another story.

The ADHD drug Ritalin helped me to begin to develop daily routines and organisation techniques. After about 5 years (and marriage to a very supportive and organised wife), I was able to stop the medication and manage myself with the routines and habits I had learned. It is not perfect, of course. I need to watch I don't get too stressed or disorganisation quickly takes over again."

ADHD

Attention Deficit Hyperactivity Disorder (ADHD) is a learning difficulty like autism. It makes it difficult to focus on anything even for a short time. It leads to anger and frustration at not being able to advance in life and is not always diagnosed at a young age. Once treated ADHD need not be a barrier – 18 time Olympic Gold Medal swimmer Michael Phelps has the disorder.

IS YOUR MATE OFF HIS GAME?

Stress affects mental health. Every year, one in four of us faces a mental health challenge. That's odds of 3/1 so we all know someone affected.

Because we don't really understand mental health problems, sometimes we shy away from people who have them. We pretend we're different, that these things won't affect us. But they do. They hit people just like you.

If you think a mate is bottling something up, there's a simple way to make a difference: do something together - car, computer, exercise, garden, walk, even housework.

Get him to give you a hand. Feeling wanted makes us all feel better. You don't have to talk but if you want to, doing something together makes it easier. Open up yourself - if you think he has work issues, perhaps talk about your work. Try to:

> Keep it real: take it seriously but don't make it a big deal.

> Ask 'How's it going?'.

> Keep in touch more: text or email.

> Doing stuff is as good as a chat: let your mate see that you know he's still the same person.

> Talk. Swap stories: don't ignore the difficult stuff if it comes up - you don't need to solve it or be an expert, you just need ears.

> Be there: ask if you can do anything.

> Give him this booklet.

WORKS FOR YOU?

We all have stress. Hopefully this booklet has given you something else to think about. Try one of the ideas and see how it goes. Doing something helps us feel better. Use this page to set some goals and targets for yourself.

WHO CAN HELP?

www.menshealthforum.org.uk/howRU

NHS Choices
Online 'front door' to NHS
www.nhs.uk
www.nhs.uk/livewell/mentalhealth/Pages/
Mentalhealthhome.aspx

Work
Find trade unions at
www.tuc.org.uk
Working Families
www.workingfamilies.org.uk

Money
Citizens' Advice at:
www.citizensadvice.org.uk
Money Advice Service
www.moneyadviceservice.org.uk

Online tool on money worries & mental health:
www.nhs.uk/Tools/Pages/Money-worries.aspx

Relationships
Relate   0300 100 1234
Relationship counselling (also help with sex/
porn addiction)
www.relate.org.uk

Domestic Violence
Men's Advice Line (for victims)
9-5 Mon-Fri   0808 801 0327
www.mensadviceline.org.uk

Respect (for perpetrators)
9-5 Mon-Fri   0808 802 4040
www.respectphoneline.org.uk

Drink and Drugs
Addaction   020 7251 5860
www.addaction.org.uk

Alcoholics Anonymous   0800 9177 650
www.alcoholics-anonymous.co.uk

Adfam - if a mate/family member has drink
problems
http://www.adfam.org.uk

UK Narcotics Anonymous   0300 999 12 12
www.ukna.org

www.nhs.uk/livewell/drugs/pages/drugshome.
aspx

Other addictions
Gamcare (Gambling)   0808 8020 133
www.gamcare.org.uk

Gamblers Anonymous
www.gamblersanonymous.org.uk

LADIES   GENTS   GENTS WITH ANGER ISSUES

NHS -sex and love addiction
http://www.nhs.uk/chq/pages/3053.aspx

Sex & Love Addicts Anonymous   07984 977 884
www.slaauk.org

Sexuality
Lesbian and Gay Foundation   0345 330 3030
www.lgf.org.uk

Volunteering
Volunteering England
www.ncvo.org.uk
Do It Volunteering
www.do-it.org.uk

Exercise for depression
NHS
www.nhs.uk/Conditions/stress-anxiety-depression/Pages/exercise-for-depression.aspx

Anger
NHS
http://www.nhs.uk/Conditions/stress-anxiety-depression/Pages/controlling-anger.aspx

British Association of Anger Management
www.angermanage.co.uk

Seasonal Affective Disorder
SADA
www.sada.org.uk

Eating Disorders
Beat   0808 801 0677
www.b-eat.co.uk
Men Get Eating Disorders Too
www.mengetedstoo.co.uk

Bereavement
Cruse Bereavement Care   0808 808 1677
www.cruse.org.uk

Cognitive Behavioural Therapy
Living Life To The Full
www.llttf.com
Beating the Blues
www.beatingtheblues.co.uk

Mindfulness
To find a course near you:
http://bemindful.co.uk

Counselling
Counselling Directory   0333 3447 990
www.counselling-directory.org.uk

Other
Calm   0800 58 58 58
Service specifically for men
www.thecalmzone.net

Mind   0300 123 3393
www.mind.org.uk

Rethink   0300 5000 927
For people with severe mental illness
www.rethink.org

Saneline   0300 304 7000
For anyone affected by mental illness, including
family, friends and carers
www.sane.org.uk

UK ADHD partnership
www.ukadhd.com

Mencap (the voice of learning disability)
www.mencap.org.uk

National Autistic Society
www.autism.org.uk

Plus You Tube clip on diaphragmatic breathing:
http://www.youtube.com/watch?v=_TUZiiMy1iI

PHOTO CREDITS: Dave McCairley, istockphoto. Thanks also to: Casey Fleser, Travis Rigel Lukas Hornung, Elliott P, Reg Natarajan, Navaneeth KN, and Bare Knuckle Yellow who were all kind enough to make their images available through the Creative Commons for modification and commercial use. (If this is not the case, please contact us.)

NEED HEALTH INFO?

IT'S FREE AND EASY AT THE MEN'S HEALTH FORUM WEBSITE

On the Men's Health Forum website, you can:

> find information on mental health issues and links to other common conditions affecting men

> find answers to pretty much every question you could possibly ask about the penis

> read about the health experiences of other men

> search for local health services and sports/exercise facilities in your area

> use our Man MOT chat service if you live or work in an area in which the service is operating.

VISIT MENSHEALTHFORUM.ORG.UK